The Greatest Inventors in History

Activity Wizo

Please consider writing a review!

Just visit: activitywizo.com/review

Have questions? We want to hear from you!

Email us at: support@activitywizo.com

ISBN: 978-1-951806-43-9

FREE BONUS

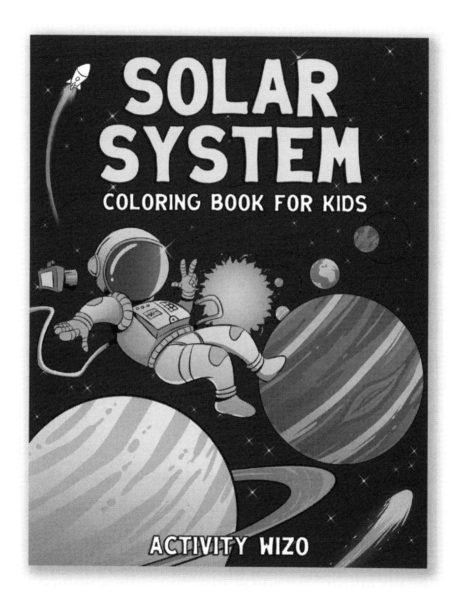

Get This FREE Bonus Now!

Just go to: activitywizo.com/free

Table of Contents

Leonardo da Vinci

Today, we use the phrase "Renaissance Man" to describe a person who is skilled in several different fields. This phrase originates from the Italian Renaissance, a time when art and science weren't considered different areas of study but two parts of the same discipline. A Renaissance artist wasn't just skilled in drawing, painting, and sculpting. They also studied music, mathematics, science, medicine, literature, and inventing. And nobody from the Italian Renaissance sums up the "Renaissance Man" concept better than Leonardo da Vinci.

The son of a notary and a peasant woman, Leonardo da Vinci was born near Florence, Italy on April 15, 1452. Though da Vinci's artistic talent was clear at an early age, he didn't receive a formal education. He did have an endless passion for learning, however, and taught himself everything from engineering and physics to astronomy and human anatomy. He studied science so he could become a better artist, but he also used his artistic skills to become a better scientist.

Before da Vinci's lifetime there was no formal way to draw mechanical objects, so he had to invent one. He was the first person to develop a process called "technical drawing." In his journals, da Vinci produced hundreds of technical drawings to describe his inventions. Many of these inventions were so ahead of their time that they couldn't be built for hundreds of years. Over the course of his lifetime, he came up with ideas for at least seventeen different inventions that we still use today.

For most of his life, da Vinci was interested in the possibility of human flight. He's often credited with inventing the world's first helicopter. His "Air Screw" was a flying machine with fifteen-foot wide rotors that spun to produce liftoff. Since modern helicopters weren't introduced until the 1940s, the Air Screw was over four hundred years ahead of its time. In addition to the Air Screw, da Vinci came up with another flying machine called an "ornithopter," which used flapping wings to produce flight, as well as a version of a parachute with a wooden frame.

Although da Vinci disliked violence, he was often hired to create inventions for the military. In fact, he invented the first version of a tank. This heavily armored vehicle needed eight men to operate it, and it featured thirty-six guns. He created the world's first machine gun, a firearm that used twelve rotating barrels to fire almost continuously. For naval warfare, da Vinci invented a suit with a breathing hose that allowed a user to sabotage an enemy boat under water. This was the first version of the modern diving suit. Da Vinci even created one of the world's first robots. He designed and possibly built his "mechanical knight" in 1495; it was reportedly capable of sitting, standing, and moving its head.

But da Vinci also invented many objects used in everyday life. He invented the anemometer, an instrument used to determine wind speed; a rotating bridge; ball bearings; a cart that could be propelled without a horse; and a hybrid musical instrument called a viola organista, which used parts from a harpsichord, organ, and viola.

If Leonardo da Vinci had only been an artist, he still would have been remembered forever thanks to masterpieces like his iconic painting *The Mona Lisa* and his famous sculpture *Pieta*. But his inventions prove that he's one of the world's most original geniuses, and a true Renaissance Man.

Thomas Edison

Many people consider Thomas Edison to be the greatest inventor of all time. Today, we give him credit for inventing everything from the light bulb to the movie camera to the phonograph. In reality, other people came up with the ideas for these inventions first. But Thomas Edison perfected them and made them available to millions of consumers.

Thomas Alva Edison was born on February 11, 1847, in Milan, Ohio. By the time he was thirteen years old, a series of illnesses had left him nearly deaf. Edison only attended school for three months, but he loved to learn and he read every book he could get his hands on. While working as a railroad telegraph operator, Edison spent his nights coming up with new inventions. His first two inventions were improved versions of a vote counting machine and a stock ticker. When he was thirty years old, Edison started his first laboratory in Menlo Park, New Jersey.

In 1877, even though he was nearly deaf, Edison invented a machine that could record sound called the phonograph. The first version of his phonograph used tinfoil, but later versions recorded sounds onto wax cylinders. Edison spent the next fifty years of his life improving the phonograph. And he became the first person in history to record his own voice when he recorded himself singing "Mary Had a Little Lamb." The success of the phonograph earned him the nickname "The Wizard of Menlo Park."

In 1878, Edison began working on a new light bulb. Although other people had worked on electric lights for decades, Edison's light bulb was the first that could be produced in large amounts.

But before Edison could sell his light bulb, the public first needed electricity in their homes. During the 1880s, scientists argued over whether the best type of electricity to use was alternating current (AC) or direct current (DC). While Edison's light bulb used DC, many other inventors like Nikola Tesla preferred AC. In the end, Tesla and his business partner George Westinghouse won out, and AC is used in most homes today.

In the 1890s, Edison's focus moved to motion pictures. Along with an associate named W.K.L. Dickson, Edison invented an improved movie camera called the Kinetoscope. Thanks to the Kinetoscope, he became one of the first influential figures in the movie industry. His companies produced over twelve hundred films, including the classic *The Great Train Robbery*.

In his later life, Edison and his company branched out into even more industries. In 1912, he teamed up with fellow inventor Henry Ford to create a battery for Ford's Model T car. He also developed technology for the United States mining industry during World War II.

Edison kept working into his eighties. In his lifetime, he held one thousand ninety-three patents and founded General Electric, one of the largest companies in the world. Today, General Electric still makes many products people use in their homes.

Thomas Edison

Alexander Graham Bell

When it comes to inventions, history has a way of giving too much credit to one person. Today, Alexander Graham Bell gets credit for inventing the telephone. Just as Thomas Edison wasn't the only person to invent the light bulb, Bell wasn't solely responsible for the invention of the telephone. But he did make many significant contributions to the telephone. And the telephone was just one of several important technologies he invented.

Alexander Graham Bell was born on March 3, 1847, in Edinburgh, Scotland. His mother, Eliza Grace Symonds, was nearly deaf due to a childhood illness. Because of this, Bell spent much of his life working for the deaf. He was also a scientist and inventor, and he spent much of his spare time experimenting and improving existing inventions.

In 1868, Joseph Stearns invented an early version of the telegraph, a machine that can send written messages over wires. Many inventors, including Bell and his rival Elisha Gray, spent the next several years improving the telegraph's design. From 1871 to 1874, Bell developed a machine called a "harmonic telegraph," which allowed multiple messages to be sent at the same time.

During this time, Bell and others became interested in a new concept: the possibility of transmitting sound over wires. While perfecting his harmonic telegraph, Bell also worked on a new invention he called the telephone. Bell was awarded the patent for the telephone on March 7, 1876. Three days later he made the first official phone call in history when he called his assistant and said, "Mr. Watson, come here, I need you."

After Bell was awarded the patent, other inventors (including Elisha Gray) argued that they should be given credit. The patent office acknowledged that Gray had been working on a similar design but refused to reverse its decision. Over his lifetime, inventors filed over six hundred lawsuits against Bell's patent, but it was upheld. Today, the consensus is that Bell and Gray most likely invented the telephone independently of each other.

After his success with the telephone, Bell co-founded the Bell Telephone Company, but he began to focus on other inventions. With the wealth he earned from the telephone, Bell founded the Volta Institution, a scientific laboratory that studied deafness and developed new technology. In the 1880s and 1890s, the Volta Laboratory made many important breakthroughs including: a perfected version of the gramophone, an early version of the metal detector, and an early wireless telephone called the "photophone."

Bell died in 1922. Two years later, engineers at Bell Telephone created a new unit of measurement for sound. In honor of Bell, they named it the "decibel."

Benjamin Franklin

Many of the inventors in this collection devoted their entire lives to scientific discovery, which allowed them to produce their greatest inventions. Benjamin Franklin, on the other hand, held many different careers. He was a newspaper publisher and editor. He was a political activist who fought for American independence from Great Britain. He was one of America's most important diplomats, and he played a major role in drafting the American constitution. Somehow, in the middle of all this work, he also found time to invent several devices that are still in use today.

Benjamin Franklin was born on January 17, 1706. When he was just eleven years old he made his first invention, a set of swim fins. But he didn't become a full-time inventor until 1743. That year, Franklin published a pamphlet, titled "A Proposal for Promoting Useful Knowledge," which encouraged his readers to pursue scientific discoveries. Leading by example, he left his printing business to a partner and focused on inventing.

Lightning was not well understood in Franklin's time, making it dangerous to people and buildings. In 1749, Franklin began to study lightning to figure out how to control it. One night in 1752, Franklin attached a key to a kite string and flew the kite in a lightning storm. The kite wasn't struck by lightning, but it did attract an electrical charge from the storm. Franklin's experiment proved that lightning was made of electricity, which led to the invention of the lightning rod. This is a metal pole attached to a building that attracts lightning strikes and redirects them into the ground.

After the lightning rod, Franklin looked for other ways to improve the world. Before Franklin, stoves required large amounts of wood and were often a fire hazard. Franklin invented the "Franklin stove." The Franklin stove stood in the middle of the room and provided more heat and used less fuel. He created the first bifocal, an eyeglass lens that helps people see things clearly whether they're up close or far away. He invented a musical instrument called a "glass armonica." And when his brother James developed kidney stones, Franklin invented the world's first catheter.

Above all, Benjamin Franklin became an inventor to make people's lives better. He refused patents for many of his inventions because he wanted them to be available for everybody.

Archimedes

The ancient Greek scientist Archimedes is the earliest inventor on our list. Since he lived over 2,200 years ago, we don't know much about his childhood or his early life. He was most likely born in the year 287 B.C.E. in the Greek city of Syracuse, which is in present-day Sicily, Italy. The surviving stories about him are most likely untrue, but they still reflect his reputation as one of the greatest scientists of his time.

Archimedes was primarily a mathematician who used math to observe the world. Math was a relatively new subject, and many of Archimedes's discoveries about the natural world are still true today. For example, he discovered how to calculate the volume and surface area of a sphere. He discovered a more accurate way to calculate pi, which was used into the twentieth century. And he discovered the forces that make levers and pulleys work.

His most famous mathematical discovery was a way to calculate the volume of an object, or the amount of space it takes up. Archimedes supposedly made this discovery when King Hiero I of Syracuse asked him to figure out how much gold and silver was in his crown. According to legend, Archimedes was stumped until one day he took a bath. When he got into the bathtub, he noticed that the water level rose, and he realized that the displaced water could be used to calculate his body's volume. The discovery caused Archimedes to run naked through the streets shouting "Eureka!"

Archimedes used his mathematical observations to create inventions to improve the world. His most famous invention was the "Archimedes Screw," a device that made water easier to collect. By placing a large screw inside a cylinder and then turning it, the Archimedes Screw brings water to the Earth's surface. He's also credited with inventing a version of the odometer, which many cars still have today.

Archimedes contributed even more inventions to warfare. The city of Syracuse was famous for being difficult to conquer, and that's mainly thanks to Archimedes and his inventions. He invented an improved version of the catapult that could launch heavy objects like trees and boulders over large distances. In one battle, Archimedes supposedly defeated a fleet of Roman ships by using reflections from large mirrors to set them on fire.

Like many stories about Archimedes's life, this one is probably a myth. But his achievements and discoveries were so important that we still remember him today.

Louis Pasteur

The world is covered in trillions of organisms, called bacteria, so tiny they can't be seen with the naked eye. Most bacteria are harmless to people. Some bacteria are helpful to humans, like the bacteria in our stomachs that help us digest food. Other kinds of bacteria can be dangerous, like the *e. Coli* bacteria found in raw foods. The wrong bacteria can make food spoil, or even cause disease. But, thanks to Louis Pasteur, bacteria aren't nearly as dangerous as they used to be.

Pasteur was born on December 22, 1822, in Dole, France. Though he was an average student, he earned a doctorate in 1847. A year later he became a professor of chemistry at Strasbourg University, where he made important discoveries about the properties of tartrates.

Alcoholic beverages have existed for thousands of years, and they're created with a process called fermentation. But before Pasteur's time, fermentation wasn't well understood. Most scientists believed fermentation was caused by a process called "spontaneous generation." Pasteur proved that fermentation is actually caused when bacteria digests the sugar found in yeast and other carbohydrates.

Though Pasteur's discovery changed the wine and beer industries, it had an even bigger effect than that. In addition to fermentation, bacteria can also cause wine, beer, and other foods and drinks to spoil. In 1862, while researching the harmful bacteria found in wine and beer, Pasteur invented a process called "pasteurization." During this process, wine and beer are heated to kill harmful bacteria. Pasteurization was soon used to make other foods and drinks—like milk—safer. Today, almost all perishable food in the world is pasteurized before it is sold.

After his success with pasteurization, Pasteur's focus turned to curing diseases. As with fermentation, the cause of disease was not well understood before Pasteur. Unlike many scientists of his time, Pasteur was a believer in "germ theory," which says that disease is caused when microscopic organisms enter the body.

In 1879, Pasteur made an important breakthrough in the fight against disease. While studying a type of cholera that infects chicken, Pasteur discovered that injecting chickens with a weaker form of cholera made them immune to the disease. This process is called vaccination. Although Pasteur wasn't the first person to develop a vaccine, his discovery proved that it could treat diseases. This discovery led Pasteur to develop vaccines for anthrax and rabies.

The discovery of vaccines made Pasteur even more famous. In 1888, he founded the Pasteur Institute, a research organization still in operation today. His contributions to food safety and disease treatment have made him one of the most important scientists of all time.

Alexander Fleming

Many of the world's greatest discoveries happen after a scientist (or a team of scientists) spends years researching and experimenting until they make a breakthrough. But, sometimes a major scientific discovery can happen by accident. That's how Alexander Fleming discovered penicillin, one of the biggest medical breakthroughs of the twentieth century.

The discovery of penicillin, however, was just one of Alexander Fleming's accomplishments. He was born on August 6, 1881, in East Ayrshire, Scotland, and in 1895, he moved to London to live with his older brother. In 1901, he joined the Territorial Army, where he would serve in the London Scottish Regiment for the next thirteen years. During this time, he also began to study medicine. An excellent student, he first planned to become a surgeon. But he switched his specialty to a new field called "bacteriology."

A bacteriologist is a scientist who studies bacteria. Bacteria are the tiny organisms that cover nearly everything in the world and often cause infections in humans, especially if it gets into a wound. Before Alexander Fleming's time, bacteria wasn't well understood and few people believed it could cause disease. Even worse, few medicines existed that could kill bacteria.

When World War I broke out in 1914, Fleming was sent to France where he set up a lab to study bacterial infections in the wounded. This was when he made his first big medical discovery. Fleming noticed that the medicines being used to kill bacteria were also harming the soldiers' immune systems. He recommended using saline solution instead, and this saved many lives.

After the war, Fleming returned to England where he made his second big medical discovery--and this one was by accident. In 1921, Fleming was sick with a cold, and a drop of mucus from his nose dripped onto bacteria he was studying. A few weeks later, Fleming discovered his mucus had killed the bacteria. This led to the discovery of lysozome, an enzyme in our immune systems that helps fight infection.

Seven years later, Fleming made another discovery by accident. In the summer of 1928, Fleming was studying a culture of bacteria called *Staphylococcus aureus* when he went on vacation with his family. When he returned a month later, he discovered that mold in his lab had killed the bacteria. This mold is called *Penicillium notatum*, or penicillin.

Fleming and his team quickly discovered that penicillin could kill many other types of bacteria that cause illness—and without harming the patient. Later, two other scientists, Dr. Howard Florey and Dr. Ernst Chain, created a vaccine from the mold.

The discovery of penicillin completely changed the way doctors fight infection. Before penicillin, infections killed more soldiers than combat. But During World War II, Florey traveled to the United States and convinced the government to produce penicillin in large amounts. Throughout the war, penicillin saved hundreds of thousands of lives.

In 1945, Fleming, Florey, and Chain shared the Nobel Prize. Fleming himself became one of the most famous scientists in the world for his role in the discovery. And it all happened because he didn't wash a petri dish before he went on vacation.

Nikola Tesla

To understand Nikola Tesla, it helps to compare him with Thomas Edison. Both men were brilliant inventors, and both of them helped figure out how to harness the power of electricity. But, unlike Tesla, Edison was also a brilliant businessman and promoter. Because of this, Edison has often gotten more credit for his achievements. More recently, however, historians have given Tesla the credit he deserves.

Tesla was born on either June 9 or 10, 1856, in Smiljan, Croatia, in what was then the Austro-Hungarian Empire. At a young age, he began showing signs of mental illness that would affect him for the rest of his life. He studied engineering at the University of Prague and at the University of Graz, in Austria.

At the time, there were two competing systems of electrical currents: alternating current, or AC, which is high voltage, and the lower-voltage direct current, or DC. AC is more powerful and can be used to electrify a larger area, but it's also more dangerous. DC, on the other hand, is less powerful but safer. While Tesla was at university, he became a believer in AC.

In 1884, Tesla moved to New York City to work as an engineer for Thomas Edison, who was a believer in DC. Edison respected Tesla's talents, but they were very different people. Edison once promised Tesla fifty thousand dollars to improve the design of one of his DC power generators, which Tesla did, but Edison never paid him. Tesla quit Edison's company after just one year.

Tesla tried to start his own company, but it was unsuccessful. He did, however, meet an engineer and inventor named George Westinghouse. Westinghouse had built the country's first AC power system in Boston, and he hired Tesla to develop more AC projects. During this time, Tesla's work flourished. Between 1887 and 1888, he received over thirty patents for his inventions. His most successful was the world's first AC motor.

After the invention of the AC motor, Tesla and Westinghouse became Thomas Edison's main rivals. The main issue was whether to set up cities' electrical systems using AC or DC. In the end, Tesla and Westinghouse won out, and the AC system became the dominant form of electricity.

Tesla's inventions made him rich, and he had enough money to finally fund his own projects. In 1891, he invented a high-voltage electrical transformer called the Tesla coil, which is still used today in many TV sets and radios. In 1893, he built the world's first modern power station at Niagara Falls. He performed some of the first experiments with X-rays and radio transmission. And, in 1898, he invented a radio-controlled boat and demonstrated it at Madison Square Garden.

By the end of his life, Tesla had received nearly three hundred patents for his inventions. His AC power systems became the standard for cities around the world, and we still use them today.

Timothy Berners-Lee

The Internet is such a part of everyday life that it can be difficult to imagine the world without it. But the Internet did start somewhere—with a British computer scientist named Timothy Berners-Lee.

Timothy Berners-Lee was born on June 8, 1955, in London, England. In the 1950s, few people even knew what a computer was. But computers were a big part of Berners-Lee's life because both of his parents, Mary Lee Woods and Conway Berners-Lee, were computer scientists. His parents helped build the Ferranti Mark I, the first computer sold commercially. When the first Ferranti Mark I was sold to Manchester University in 1951, it had only 82 kilobytes of storage. Its CPU was housed in two storage bays that were seven feet high, three feet wide, and fifteen feet long--big enough to fill up a room.

Berners-Lee was gifted with computers from an early age. While he was a student at Oxford University, he built a computer out of an old TV set. After he graduated in 1976, Berners-Lee followed his parents into computer science. His first jobs were writing software for companies that were often using computers for the first time. In 1978, he wrote typesetting software that allowed computers to print documents through a printer.

In 1980, he began working for the European Organization for Nuclear Research, or CERN. The scientists at CERN used computers, but their computers were only connected by e-mail. This made it difficult to share and update large documents that made up their research. To solve this problem, Berners-Lee invented a software program called Enquire. Enquire used a process called "hypertext" to link documents to each other and make information accessible more quickly.

But about ten thousand scientists worked at CERN, and many of them had different kinds of computers; not all of them could use Enquire. Berners-Lee worked for several different companies through the 1980s, working on ways to connect computers to each other. In 1989, he returned to CERN and developed a system that allowed every computer to share hypertext documents. Berners-Lee wrote software for the first web server and the first web browser, and he created the first version of the Internet as we know it today. The first thing shared on the Internet was CERN's telephone directory. On December 20, 1990, he created the Internet's first web page, which described the project itself.

Berners-Lee knew the Internet could be used for many more purposes than linking CERN computers. He believed the Internet could be used to connect everyone in the world, and he believed it should be free to everyone. As of April 2020, it's estimated that over four and a half billion people use the Internet every day. And Timothy Berners-Lee still fights to make the Internet free for all.

Samuel Morse

Thanks to the Internet, today we can send messages around the world in less than a second. But not too long ago, sending a letter over a long distance could take weeks, months, or even longer. For example, if you wanted to send a letter across the country in 1860, the fastest the Pony Express could deliver it was ten days. But Samuel Morse made it much faster to send messages when he invented the telegraph.

Samuel Morse was born April 27, 1791, in Charlestown, Massachusetts. Many of the people in this collection were inventors for their entire lives, even during their childhood. Samuel Morse, on the other hand, started much later. He was an average student as a boy, and for the first part of his life he was a painter. In 1811, he moved to England to study painting, and in the 1820s and 30s he became one of America's best portrait artists.

But Morse was interested in many other subjects—like science, philosophy, and literature. He first became interested in electricity at a college lecture in 1809. In 1832, Morse was on a boat returning to America from France when he fell into a conversation with some scientists. The scientists had just seen a demonstration of a new device called an electromagnet. Morse learned from the scientists that electromagnets could be used to transfer electricity over long distances almost immediately—as long as they were connected by a wire. Morse realized that the high speed of electricity meant that electrical signals could be transmitted almost instantly. He just needed to invent a machine that could transfer them.

Morse was so new to inventing that he didn't even know other inventors were trying to invent the same machine. He teamed up with two partners, Leonard Gale and Alfred Vale, and for the next six years they worked on developing the telegraph.

Morse's telegraph system transmitted electric signals over metal wires. To send these signals, a telegraph operator repeatedly pressed a button on a telegraph key. The person on the other end of the telegraph could hear these pulses, even from long distances away, but that still didn't allow them to communicate with each other. To solve this problem, Morse invented Morse Code.

Morse Code converts letters and numbers into a series of dots and dashes. To send a note over a telegraph system, a telegraph operator first receives a message called a "telegram," which can be written in English or any other language. The operator then translates the telegram into Morse Code and transmits it with a telegraph key. At the other end of the line, another telegraph operator listens to the code and converts it back into words. The same letter that would have taken ten days to cross the country could now travel in seconds.

Morse demonstrated his telegraph system around the country, and in 1843, Congress built the first telegraph line from Washington, D.C. to Baltimore, Maryland. In 1844, Morse sent the first message over a commercial telegraph line when he wrote, "What hath God wrought?"

Telegraph lines were soon built around the world. In the 1920s and 30s it became one of the most popular forms of communications. Eventually, other forms of technology like telephones and the Internet made the telegraph unnecessary. But without the telegraph, and without Samuel Morse, none of it would have been possible.

Samuel Morse

Charles Babbage

Today, most of us think a "computer" is an electronic device that can do almost anything. A computer lets us communicate with each other via e-mail; a computer connects to the Internet and allows us to access almost any information in seconds. A computer can be programmed with software that can perform thousands of functions, from creating documents to running a business to editing a movie. Best of all, computers are the ultimate entertainment device—they can play games, stream TV shows and movies, and more.

But originally, the computer was a lot simpler, and it was used for just one purpose: doing math equations. Basically, the first computers were really big calculators. And we have Charles Babbage to thank for them.

Charles Babbage was born in London, England, the day after Christmas in 1791. He was interested in mathematics as a child and was a strong student, and after he graduated from Cambridge in 1814, he worked as a professor at many different universities. But Babbage was frustrated with the way math was done. As anyone who's calculated math by hand knows, it can take time, especially if it's complicated. And even the best mathematicians sometimes make mistakes. Babbage knew there had to be a way to build a machine that could solve mathematical equations much faster than a human, and without making any mistakes.

Sometime after 1813, Babbage made his first calculator. It was a simple machine and it could only do certain equations up to eight decimals. He kept working on his design, and in 1823, he came up with the idea for an invention called the Difference Engine. Babbage's Difference Engine was steam-powered and as big as a locomotive, and it could perform simple calculations up to twenty decimals. But the project was expensive and difficult and Babbage never finished it.

Money for the Difference Engine ran out in 1833, but by then Babbage had another idea for an even more complicated machine, the Analytical Engine. This is considered the first modern computer, and it could complete nearly any math equation.

To use the Analytical Engine, an operator would insert a punch card with instructions. It could store up to one thousand numbers that were fifty digits long. The next computer with memory that large wasn't built until the 1960s. But, as with the Difference Engine, the Analytical Engine was expensive and Babbage never completed it.

Although Babbage didn't complete either of his computers in his lifetime, his ideas influenced many computer designers who came after, and he's remembered today as the founder of modern computing. Really, he was just ahead of his time. In 1991, a team of researchers at London's Science Museum finally built a Difference Engine using his original designs, and it worked.

Galileo Galilei

A scientist doesn't just study the natural world to understand how it works. Humans' understanding of our world is always changing, which means that sometimes a scientist also has to challenge other people to change how they think. While Galileo made many important scientific discoveries, he also had to convince people that things they believed about science were wrong--including the way they practiced science.

Galileo Galilei was born on February 15, 1564 in Pisa, Italy. In Galileo's time, very few people ever received an education, and those who did were often educated at a monastery rather than at a school. Galileo went to a monastery run by the Camalodese Order. First, he wanted to become a monk, but later he studied medicine. Eventually, he decided to devote himself to the study of math. And, in 1589, he became the chair of mathematics at the University of Pisa.

While at the University of Pisa, Galileo began to challenge many commonly held ideas about nature. His main area of study was the principles of motion, or how objects move. By dropping two different objects off the top of the Leaning Tower of Pisa, Galileo discovered that all objects fall at the same speed regardless of their size or mass. He later proved that projectiles, like a boulder launched from a catapult, always travel in a parabola shape. But above all, Galileo's biggest contribution to science during this period was the practice of using math to describe the world and its natural forces. Before this, philosophers and scientists would only use logical arguments.

In 1609, Europe was abuzz thanks to the invention of a new device: the spyglass, which makes faraway objects appear closer. Galileo was interested in the spyglass's potential, and he began working on his own design to improve it. The existing spyglass could make objects appear three times larger, but Galileo produced one that same year that could make objects appear twenty times bigger. This was the first telescope, and it allowed Galileo to study astronomy.

Using his new telescope, Galileo became the first person in history who could see faraway planets and moons up close. He discovered that the moon's surface wasn't smooth like people thought but covered in craters. He discovered four of Saturn's moons: Callisto, Io, Europa, and Ganymede. And he also discovered that the galaxy contains millions more stars than people could see without magnification.

Galileo combined his study of motion with his study of astronomy and made his most controversial discovery yet: that the Earth rotates around the Sun. Before Galileo, most people believed that the Sun rotated around the Earth, and that the Earth was the center of the universe. Galileo's discovery outraged most of Europe, and in 1633, Pope Urban VIII held an Inquisition against him. During the trial, Galileo was forced to say his theory was wrong and that the Sun rotates around the Earth. It took three hundred more years for the Catholic Church to admit Galileo was right.

Galileo made many discoveries in his lifetime, but his idea to use math to describe nature changed the way science experiments were done. Mathematics allowed for precise measurements of natural forces, and they allowed scientists everywhere to repeat each other's experiments. Astronomers today owe a debt to Galileo, scientists too.

Stephanie Kwolek

The greatest inventions don't always have to be an idea nobody's ever thought of before. Sometimes, they can just be a way to improve a process that already exists. Chemist Stephanie Kwolek's research into artificial fabrics has led to hundreds of products that never would have been possible otherwise, and it's saved countless lives.

Stephanie Kwolek was born on July 31, 1923, in New Kensington, Pennsylvania. Her father worked in a foundry and taught her how to explore and observe nature. Her mother was a seamstress and taught Stephanie how to appreciate fashion. At a time when relatively few women were allowed to go to college, Kwolek graduated from the Carnegie Institute of Technology with a degree in chemistry. Due to a shortage of male workers after World War II, Kwolek went to work for the chemical company DuPont. She only planned to work there for a short time, but she found artificial fabrics to be so interesting that she wound up staying for over forty years.

Kwolek's research was focused on "aramids," a kind of polymer that can be turned into strong, stiff fibers. Kwolek realized these fibers could be turned into fabrics that could protect people in dangerous environments. In 1961, Kwolek invented a new kind of fabric that could resist fires. DuPont released the fabric under the name "Nomex." Today, Nomex is still used to make garments for firefighters and other first responders who might come into contact with a fire.

Following her invention of Nomex, Kwolek invented another fabric that was even stiffer and stronger. Its name was "poly-p phenylene terepthalamide," but DuPont released it under the name Kevlar.

Kevlar is most famous for being the material used to make bulletproof vests, but it's so strong and lightweight that it has many different uses. It's used to make panels for fighter planes and hulls for boats. It's used to strengthen fuel tanks in race cars, and it protects bike tires from puncturing. It's even used to make everyday objects like cell phone cases, skateboards, surf boards, hockey sticks, and ping-pong paddles.

The invention of Kevlar made DuPont billions of dollars, and it made Kwolek famous. In 1995, DuPont awarded her the Lavoisier Medal, and she's still the only female employee to receive it. That same year, she became the fourth woman to be inducted into the National Inventors Hall of Fame. She continues to be an inspiration to people everywhere.

Rudolph Diesel

Today, most cars run on either gasoline or electricity, but for most of the twentieth century, almost every car ran on gas. But if it weren't for an engineer named Rudolph Diesel, our cars might run on steam--or, we might not have cars at all.

Rudolph Diesel was born in Paris, France—although both his parents were German—on March18, 1858. Rudolph and his family lived in France until the outbreak of the Franco-Prussian War in 1870, which forced them to return to Germany. In his school days, the young Diesel was an excellent engineering student, and when he graduated from university he became an engineer. He spent his first professional years working with Carl von Linde, an engineer who pioneered refrigeration.

Diesel was born right after the end of the first Industrial Revolution. James Watt's invention of the steam engine completely changed the way society worked. But the problem with a steam engine is that up to 90 percent of the energy it produces is wasted. Many engineers and inventors knew that the steam engine could be even more powerful. In 1876, another German engineer named Nicolaus Otto invented the Otto engine, the world's first engine that ran on petroleum. But Otto never planned for his engine to be used for transportation.

After leaving Carl von Linde's laboratory, Diesel also explored ways to make a more powerful engine. He built a steam engine that ran on ammonia vapor, but he had to abandon the idea when his engine exploded and nearly killed him. Eventually, he settled on the idea to build a gas-powered engine that could power vehicles.

Beginning in 1890, Diesel created several engine designs. And, in 1897, he debuted a 25-horsepower engine that was more efficient than any engine that had come before. Unlike steam engines of the time, which only used 10 percent of the energy they created, the first diesel engine used 25 percent. Today's diesel engines run at 50 percent efficiency. But at the time, this was a big achievement.

The invention was a success and made him famous. Because diesel fuel was less likely to explode than other kinds of fuel, militaries around Europe found applications for his engine. In 1904, the French military began using his engines in their submarines.

After World War I, countries around the world began using diesel engines for all sorts of applications. Diesel-powered trucks were invented in the 1920s, followed by diesel-powered trains in the 1930s, and in 1939, 25 percent of the world's sea trade ran on diesel.

Diesel was such a visionary that he even predicted that engines could run on vegetable oils instead of petroleum products. In the 1970s and 1980s, Diesel was proven right when vegetable oil became a viable substitute for gasoline in some vehicles.

Cai Lun

In the twenty-first century, much of the world has been switching from paper to digital as a way to conserve natural resources. But for two thousand years, paper was the most widely used writing surface. Paper is one of the most important discoveries in human history. It's allowed us to communicate with each other, preserve knowledge for future generations, keep track of our economies, and create moving works of art. And it's all thanks to Cai Lun.

Cai Lun, or Ts'ai Lun as his name is also spelled, lived so long ago that many details about his life are unknown, even his birthday. He's thought to have been born between the years 50 and 62 A.D., in Guiyang, a city in the Hunan province of China. He was born into a poor family during the time of the Eastern Han Dynasty, and in 75 A.D., he became a court official under Emperor Zhang. He was closely involved in court politics under the reign of Zhang and his successor, Emperor He.

Before Cai Lun's time, people used a variety of different surfaces for writing. Some cultures carved words into stone, which takes considerable time and effort. Other cultures used dried leaves, like papyrus, but it wasn't always durable. In ancient China, silk was a common writing surface, but it was expensive and difficult to produce.

In 105 A.D., Cai Lun discovered a new writing surface that was even better than silk, and he presented it to Emperor He. Cai Lun's paper was called "mulberry paper" because it used the bark from mulberry trees as well as bamboo, hemp, cloth rags, and fishing nets. To make mulberry paper, Cai Lun mixed these ingredients together in water and pounded the mixture with a wooden tool. Then, he poured the mixture onto a piece of cloth that let the water drain out, leaving only the paper. Mulberry paper was of a higher quality than silk paper, and it was easier and cheaper to make. Emperor He was so impressed that he gave Cai Lun a title. Today, Cai Lun is considered a Chinese national hero. In China, people still burn paper over graves at funerals in Cai Lun's honor.

Paper was immediately popular, and over the next few centuries it spread to countries like Korea, Japan, and Vietnam. It made its way to Arabic countries in 751 via the Silk Road, and then into North Africa. Paper finally arrived in Europe when it was made in Moorish Spain in 1150. When the printing press was invented in 1440, it used paper to create books. Once books were able to be produced on a large scale, more and more people could be educated. Many of the inventors in this collection wouldn't have been able to make their discoveries if Cai Lun hadn't invented paper first.

Louis Braille

Reading is one of the most important skills a person can learn. Being able to read allows a person to acquire knowledge, communicate with other people, experience stories, and so much more. So much of our world is based on written words that reading is a requirement to be able to successfully participate in modern life. People have been reading and writing for thousands of years. But until relatively recently, reading was a lot more difficult for blind people—if not impossible.

Louis Braille was born January 4, 1809, in Coupvray, France, a small town near Paris. When he was just three years old, he was playing in his father's workshop when an accident caused him to go blind. But he never let his lack of sight stop him from living his life. He became a skilled musician, specializing in the organ, and in 1819 he won a scholarship to the Royal Institute for Blind Children, in Paris.

The Royal Institute for Blind Children was the first school for blind kids in the world. Before it was built, most people didn't believe that blind people could learn anything. As a result, they weren't worth educating. But a man named Valentin Haüy wanted to give blind people the same education as everybody else, so in 1785 he founded the Institute. Originally, the Institute taught blind children skills that let them get jobs. Though Hauy wasn't blind himself, he invented the first system to teach blind people how to read. His system used raised letters, similar to the ones found on coins. Blind people would "read" the letters by touching them with their fingers.

Hauy's reading system helped blind people, but it wasn't perfect. His letters were difficult to make, and blind children couldn't make them themselves, which meant they had no way to write. Louis Braille found Hauy's system difficult to use. So when he was just fifteen years old, he came up with a simpler alphabet for the blind. This alphabet was called "Braille," in his honor.

Each letter of the Braille alphabet consists of a combination of up to six bumps, which are made by pressing a pin through a piece of paper. Braille can be printed with special printers. But, even better, it's simple enough that blind children can write their own Braille words. He expanded Braille so it could be used to write musical notes, and soon he translated a popular history textbook into Braille.

Even though the Braille alphabet was an improvement on the Hauy system, the Royal Institute refused to teach it because it was already used to the Hauy system. Louis Braille became a teacher at the Institute in 1826 and taught there until he died in 1852. After his death, his students demanded that the school start teaching Braille, and in 1854, the Royal Institute finally did. Braille has been the standard alphabet for blind people ever since, and it's allowed millions of blind people to read and write like they never could before.

Louis Braille

Alessandro Volta

Electricity is a form of energy caused by the flow of charged particles called electrons. Humans have always known about electricity thanks to things like lightning bolts and electric eels. But until the seventeenth century, we haven't understood how electricity works. In the 1600s, scientists began studying electricity, which allowed them to invent things that had never been possible before. One of these scientists was Alessandro Volta, inventor of the battery.

Alessandro Volta was born February 18, 1745, in Como, Italy, the son of a noble family. He showed an interest in science at a young age, and by age eighteen he was exchanging letters with some of Italy's most important physicists. Alessandro was especially fascinated with the new discoveries that were being made about electricity.

In 1774, he became a professor of physics at the Royal School in Como. While there, he improved the design of a device called an "electrophorus," which creates static electricity. In 1776, Volta read a paper by Benjamin Franklin that described how marsh gas could be set on fire. Volta tried to isolate the source of this "flammable air," and in 1778, he discovered (and isolated) methane. Shortly after, Volta discovered that electrical charges could be used to make methane explode. This discovery would lead to the invention of the first combustion engines decades later.

Volta's idea for the battery started as an experiment by his friend, another Italian scientist named Luigi Galvani. In 1791, Galvani hooked electrodes to a frog, causing the frog's leg to twitch. Galvani believed that the frog's muscles were creating electricity, but Volta realized the muscles were only conducting the electricity transferred by the electrodes.

Volta began experimenting with different kinds of metals to see how well they conducted electricity. To do this, he would put different pieces of metal together and then place them on his tongue. This is how he came up with his first battery, or "voltaic pile." Volta's battery used alternating layers of silver and zinc, or copper and pew. These layers were separated by either paper or cloth, which was soaked in saltwater or sodium hydroxide.

Volta's battery was the first device that could create its own electrical current. Scientists around Europe quickly found many different uses for the voltaic pile. Just six weeks later, a voltaic pile was used to evaporate water into hydrogen and oxygen. This led to an entirely new field of science called "electrochemistry."

Volta demonstrated his battery to Napoleon in 1801, and Napoleon was so impressed that he made Volta a count. Volta's battery made him famous. The unit of measurement of electrical potential was named the "volt" in his honor.

Alfred Nobel

Today, the Nobel Prize is awarded every year to a scientist who makes an important contribution to scientific knowledge. It's named after a Swedish inventor who himself made many important scientific discoveries, Alfred Nobel. But while the Nobel Prize usually celebrates scientists who discover ways to help people (for example, inventing a way to treat cancer), Nobel's most famous invention was something destructive: dynamite.

Alfred Nobel was born October 21, 1833, in Stockholm, Sweden. He was a good student, and by age sixteen he could speak five languages. He first became interested in explosives thanks to his father Immanuel, who was an engineer. In 1837, Immanuel moved to St. Petersburg, Russia, where he opened a factory that built sea mines for the Russian navy. Alfred studied chemistry and went to work for his father. His father's factory prospered during the Crimean War. But when the war ended in 1854, the factory struggled to transition to peacetime operations; it went bankrupt in 1859.

Before Alfred Nobel's lifetime, gunpowder was the only kind of explosive that existed. In 1846, a new type of chemical explosive was invented called nitroglycerin. Nitroglycerin is much more powerful than gunpowder, but it's also unstable. Even a slight bump can make nitroglycerin explode, which makes it dangerous to even transport it. After his father's factory went bankrupt, Nobel moved back to Sweden. In 1863, he started experimenting with explosives. He wanted to invent a nitroglycerin explosive that was safe enough to use.

To do this, he inserted a wooden plug filled with gunpowder into an amount of nitroglycerin. By exploding the gunpowder, this would trigger the nitroglycerin to explode. In 1865, he replaced his wooden plug with another invention called a "blasting cap." This was a metal container filled with mercury fulminate. It could be detonated with either pressure or heat. The blasting cap allowed a user to time out when they wanted the explosion to happen, which guaranteed them the ability to move to a safe distance before it went off. Nobel called his invention "dynamite," after the ancient Greek word for "power." This was the first modern high explosive.

Dynamite immediately found many uses. It could blow up mountains, which made it useful for building railroad tunnels, dams, and especially mines. Dynamite made it easier to extract ore from the Earth by mining, and this ore could then be used to make most kinds of building materials, like concrete.

But dynamite was also used as a weapon. It was immediately used in the Franco-Prussian War. As Nobel became more and more famous for his invention, some people criticized him for making it easier to hurt people. Nobel's own brother Emil was actually killed in an explosion at his factory in 1864.

In his will, Nobel used his fortune from dynamite to set up the Nobel Prize, as a way to encourage more scientific innovation after his death. He never explained why he did this, but many believe it's because he wanted to be known for more than his destructive invention.

Charles Goodyear

Inventing is a difficult process that involves trial and error. Inventions rarely work perfectly on the first try, and even the best inventors usually fail dozens or even hundreds of times before they get it right. This means that inventors must be persistent. They have to keep trying, even when it seems like they'll never make their dreams a reality. And few inventors failed more times than Charles Goodyear. But Charles Goodyear's story also shows how persistence can pay off.

Charles Goodyear was born December 29, 1800, in New Haven, Connecticut. He spent the first part of his life working for his father's hardware business, and he opened his own hardware store in 1824. But his story really begins with the rubber craze of the 1830s.

The rubber found in the soles of your shoes, or the tires on your bike, actually comes from the sticky, milk-like sap found in rubber trees. Once the rubber sap is extracted, it can be stretched into many different shapes, which makes it useful for many different purposes. When Charles Goodyear was born, rubber trees were mostly found in Brazil. The Industrial Revolution brought new demand for rubber products that could be used for industry, however, and Brazil exported more and more rubber. Factories sprang up across America that made a series of brand-new rubber products.

But the rubber that existed back then wasn't perfect. It could be very sticky. Even worse, it was unstable. At higher temperatures it would melt, and at lower temperatures it would freeze. This made it impossible to rely on rubber for making tires, hoses, and many other industrial products. Rubber became less and less popular as the 1830s went on.

But Charles Goodyear believed he could find a way to make rubber work at extreme temperatures. He tried several experiments to make rubber less sticky and more durable. He tried mixing in magnesia powder to make it less sticky, but the rubber still melted. He tried treating the rubber with nitric acid, with the same result. Goodyear lost more and more money on his experiments. And his family lost everything in the financial crash of 1837. At one point, he and his family had to live in an abandoned rubber factory. It seemed that rubber just wasn't going to work.

But in 1839, Goodyear finally made a breakthrough, and it happened by accident. By this point he was mixing sulfur in with his rubber mixture. One day, he dropped his rubber and sulfur mixture on a hot stove. This time, instead of melting, the rubber hardened like leather. Goodyear had discovered that treating rubber with sulfur and heat had finally made it stable. He named this process "vulcanization." Today, rubber is usually vulcanized at temperatures of 140°–180°C.

Unfortunately for Goodyear, the discovery didn't make him rich. He received his first patent for vulcanization in 1844. But other companies soon began producing vulcanized rubber, forcing Charles to fight them in court. These battles lasted through the 1850s until his death in 1860. He never got to profit off his invention, and he died heavily in debt. The Goodyear Tire company was founded in 1898, in Akron, Ohio. It was named in his honor, even though his descendants weren't connected with the company.

The Wright Brothers

An invention is rarely invented by just one or two people. Today, we think of the Wright brothers as the inventors of the airplane, but they didn't invent it by themselves. Like many other famous inventors in this collection, the Wright brothers never would have been able to create their invention without everyone who became before them. On the other hand, the airplane wouldn't have been possible without them.

Wilbur Wright was born April 16, 1867, near Millville, Indiana. Orville Wright was born August 19, 1871, in Dayton, Ohio. Their father was a minister, and his job meant the family had to move often. Wilbur and Orville went to many different schools, and they never went to college. But at home, they were encouraged to read as many books as they could and to learn about anything they found interesting. They became known for their intellectual minds and their technical skills. When they were boys, their father once brought them a toy helicopter. This is what first made them interested in flight.

After finishing high school, the Wright brothers started a printing shop, and later a bicycle shop. In 1899, they became interested in the idea of human flight. Before airplanes existed, humans could only fly in hot-air balloons or gliders. In 1804, English inventor Sir George Cayley built the first glider that could fly with a human onboard. After Cayley, the next person to advance the glider design was the German inventor Otto Lilienthal. Between 1891 and 1896, Lilienthal flew over two thousand glider flights. The Wright brothers followed Lilienthal's career closely. When he died in a crash in 1896, they devoted themselves to human flight. Their goal was to build a new kind of motorized glider that could fly longer distances and that a pilot could control. In other words, an airplane.

The Wright brothers built a small scale version of their airplane, with wings, about five feet long. Based on their studies and their observations of birds, the Wright brothers knew their machine needed three things: wings to provide lift, a motor, and a way to balance the machine once it was in the air. They based their wings on existing glider designs. Other inventors in Europe and the United States had been inventing lighter and lighter engines, which made their airplane motor possible. As for the control, Wilbur observed buzzards and noticed how they could use their wings to re-balance themselves after a heavy gust of wind. Wilbur rigged four cords onto the wings of the airplane that the pilot could use to right the aircraft. He called this process "wing warping."

In 1900, the brothers successfully tested their model airplane in Kitty Hawk, North Carolina. It was now time to build one that could be piloted by a human being. The brothers perfected the design of their aircraft, adding things like propellers and a rudder. On December 17, 1903, Orville Wright made the first successful aircraft flight in human history when he flew one hundred twenty feet in twelve seconds.

The Wright brothers' invention started the Age of Aviation. Their invention completely changed human history, and it was so surprising that many people didn't even believe it at first. For the next several years, the brothers traveled around the world demonstrating their invention, building better and better designs, and teaching a new generation of pilots to fly. At the time of Orville's death in 1948, the brothers were considered some of the greatest inventors in American history.

James Watt

An engine is a machine that turns fuel into mechanical energy, which it uses to produce motion. The invention of engines completely changed human life. Before engines, humans could only travel as far as they could walk, or as far as an animal like a horse could take them. Engines allowed people to travel farther using less energy, and the better engines got, the more society could advance. Many of the inventions in this collection weren't even possible without the invention of the engine first. And one of the people responsible for today's modern engines was James Watt.

James Watt was born January 19, 1736 in Greenock, Scotland. His father ran a workshop that built ships and houses. Watt spent much of his time in the workshop, and this is where he first learned how to build and repair machines. When he was seventeen, he attended the University of Glasgow. There, he decided to become a manufacturer of tools used for math, like protractors and scales. He set up a workshop in Glasgow 1757, and he became friends with many scientists.

In James Watt's time, steam engines were still relatively new. A steam engine uses wood for its fuel. When the wood is burned, it produces steam, which creates motion in the engine's parts. The first steam engine was most likely invented by Spanish inventor Jerónimo de Ayanz in 1606. His engine pumped water out of mines, which can often flood.

For about one hundred fifty years, steam engines were only used as water pumps. In 1763, James Watt was repairing a Newcomen steam engine, the most popular steam pump at the time. The Newcomen steam engine housed its cylinder and condenser in the same place, which meant the cylinder was constantly being reheated and cooled. Watt realized that the cycle of constant reheating and cooling wasted about 75 percent of the energy the Newcomen engine produced, instead of converting it to mechanical energy. Watt decided to separate the cylinder and condenser into separate units.

The separate condenser allowed engines to be more powerful, efficient, and less expensive to build and maintain. Starting in 1766, he worked as a land surveyor for eight years and paused development on his engine. He returned to steam engines in 1774, and for the next several years he perfected and improved his design. In 1781, he invented a variation of his invention that could produce rotational movement. These engines were utilized in a variety of industries like textile weaving and milling.

Watt began selling his new engines to farmers and miners. The main appeal for his steam engine was that it could replace the work done by a horse. To market this idea, Watt came up with the idea of horsepower. By studying horses and ponies, Watt calculated that a horse could move about thirty-three thousand pounds a minute. The idea stuck, and it's still used to advertise cars and trucks today.

Watt might not have invented the engine by himself, but his improvements allowed the Industrial Revolution to begin. In his honor, a unit of power called the watt was named after him.

Johannes Gutenberg

Few inventions have been as important as Johannes Gutenberg's printing press. Before Gutenberg's time, most writing was done by hand, which meant that producing a book-length piece of writing took time and money. Instead of handwriting, bookmakers could use a printing system called woodblock carving. But this was also expensive, time consuming, and unreliable. When Gutenberg invented the printing press, he found a way to print books faster, easier, and cheaper, and it completely changed the world.

Not much is known about Johannes Gutenberg's early life. He was born in Mainz, German, between 1390 and 1399 A.D. He was born into a wealthy patrician family, and he worked as both a goldsmith (which is a metal worker who specializes in gold) and a gem cutter (which is someone who takes raw precious stones and carves them into shapes for sale). He also worked on inventions that could be used to start new businesses. In 1438, some of Gutenberg's business partners sued him because he wasn't sharing his plans for a new, secret invention. This was most likely the printing press.

In the late Middle Ages, more and more people were learning how to read. This led to an increased demand for books, and Gutenberg was attempting to meet that need with his printing press. Most likely, he based his designs on the wine press, a machine used to press grapes to turn them into wine.

Gutenberg's printing press also made several improvements to the way texts were printed. The main change was moving away from wooden molds of letters, which had to be carved by hand, and instead using metal molds of letters. These metal molds were much more durable, created a higher quality text, and they could be moved around repeatedly. Gutenberg also developed a new formula for an oil-based ink that worked better with his metal molds. Additionally, he came up with a new process to flatten paper to use in printing, which also used a wine press.

We don't know exactly when Gutenberg started working on the printing press, but it was in operation by 1450. The first thing he ever printed was most likely a poem titled "The Sibyl's Prophecy," which he most likely printed to test his invention. But the first text he produced for sale was the Bible. The Gutenberg Bible was first printed in 1455. Each page featured forty-two lines of text and color illustrations. Pope Pius II praised the Gutenberg Bible, and this made it popular throughout Europe.

After the Gutenberg Bible, the world changed forever. Before Gutenberg, books were expensive, which meant that only wealthy people or church officials could afford them. Gutenberg's printing press meant that books could be printed more quickly for less money, which made them cheaper and more affordable to more people. More books meant that more people could learn how to read, which meant that more people could go to school and learn skills. With these new skills, people could start new businesses, and existing businesses could hire more educated workers. Economies grew, more people prospered, and a new middle class arrived. Books also made it easier to spread and share ideas—like ideas for new inventions. Technology grew more and more powerful, and society advanced to the point where it is today. Most of modern life wouldn't have been possible without Johannes Gutenberg.

Joseph-Marie Jacquard

Many of the world's greatest inventions were created for a very simple reason: to improve an existing process. Today, when we look back on an invention like the printing press or the steam engine, it's easy to recognize how it improved the world over hundreds of years. But to the people who were alive when these innovations were created, new inventions were often threatening. Making a process easier often means building a machine that can do the same job as a worker, but faster and more efficiently. This is great news for the person who owns the machine, but that worker might lose their job. Often, inventions that changed the world were first met with hostility. This was what happened with Joseph-Marie Jacquard's loom.

Jacquard was born on July 7, 1752 in Lyon, France. At the time of Jacquard's birth, France was one of the world's biggest manufacturers of textiles, or fabrics, but not as big as its neighbor, England. Simple fabrics could be made with machines called looms. But more complicated fabrics, especially ones with patterns, still had to be woven by hand. This made them expensive luxury items.

Like many children in France in the 1700s, Joseph-Marie Jacquard didn't receive an education, and he couldn't read until he was thirteen. When he was just a child, he went to work in a textile factory as "draw boy." A draw boy's job was boring and dangerous. Draw boys would sit on the top of the loom while the weaver operated it. While the loom's shuttle moved side to side, the draw boy had to quickly lay down threads by hand. If a draw boy didn't move fast enough, he could be seriously hurt.

Knowing how dangerous a draw boy's life could be, Jacquard wanted to invent a way for the loom to do the draw boy's job automatically. He was promoted to the job of mill mechanic, and in 1790, he started working on a new loom. Jacquard's idea added an attachment to the loom that controlled the direction of the shuttle using punch cards, which are pieces of paper with holes punched in them.

Then the French Revolution broke out, forcing Jacquard to halt his work and fight with the rebels to defend Lyon. After the Revolution, Jacquard returned to his invention, and in 1801, he finally debuted his loom. Jacquard's loom could produce even the most complicated patterns at about the same speed it could produce simple patterns, and no draw boys were required. He received a bronze medal for the loom in 1801, and he worked on perfecting it during the next several years. In 1805, he officially received a patent for the loom.

Most people in France didn't love Jacquard's loom right away. Many experienced textile weavers worried that the faster and more efficient loom would eliminate their jobs. Starting in 1801, weavers rioted in protest against the loom, and mobs tried to destroy every Jacquard loom they could find. But eventually, the textile industry realized how much of an improvement Jacquard's creation was and it became more popular. By 1810, France had finally caught up to England in textile manufacturing.

Jacquard's loom made him famous, and it brought wealth both to him personally and to his nation. But his loom attachment didn't just improve the textile industry. It also introduced the concept of programming, which is the process of giving a machine instructions so that it can complete a task on its own. Jacquard's punch card system inspired future inventors like Charles Babbage to experiment with more programmable machines, which eventually led to modern computers.

Joseph-Marie Jacquard

John Loudon McAdam

Some inventions are only possible once another invention has already been created. For example, our system of interconnected highways has made it possible to transport goods and people across greater distances in shorter amounts of time, which has led to economic growth and prosperity. But none of this would have been possible without the invention of the paved road first. And the man responsible for today's modern roads is John Loudon McAdam.

McAdam was born September 21, 1752 in Ayr, Scotland. In 1770, when he was just fourteen years old, he moved to New York City to work in his uncle's counting house, where he sold goods confiscated from the British during the Revolutionary War. In 1783, he returned to Scotland wealthy and bought an estate. He was also put in charge of building local roads.

Paved roads actually had existed long before McAdam's time. During the Roman Empire, the Romans built about 50,000 miles of roads paved with concrete, mostly for military purposes. But after the fall of the Roman Empire, their roads fell into disuses and were neglected through the Middle Ages. By McAdam's time, only remnants of the Roman road network remained, and most of the knowledge needed to build it had been lost. Essentially, McAdam was starting from scratch.

McAdam quickly realized that the roads were in bad shape. Ordinarily, roads were built by selecting a path through the countryside and clearing away all the rocks and plants. Most roads in the United Kingdom were made of dirt, which meant a rainstorm could flood them, or a snowstorm could freeze them over. Some roads in McAdam's time were made with large flat stones. But even stone roads were still uneven, and the stones would often break.

McAdam studied the problem and arrived at two conclusions: One, roads needed to be higher than the surrounding ground, or else they could flood easily. And two, the large flat stones should be replaced with layers of rocks and gravel, which would create a more uniform surface.

He spent several years perfecting his new road design, which eventually came to be called the macadam system. To build a macadam road, McAdam would clear away the ground and dig drainage ditches on both sides. He first added a layer of large flat stones, and then topped it with two more layers of gravel. The top layer of gravel was laid down in a slightly convex shape called a "camber," which helped rainwater drain more easily. Lastly, a metal roller (similar to a modern steamroller) would flatten the road. Passing traffic would further compact the road and make the surface even flatter and smoother.

In 1802, McAdam moved to Bristol and became the surveyor of local roads. For the next several years, he built macadam roads in the area. And in 1816 and 1819, he wrote two books explaining how to build them. In 1820, he was appointed Surveyor General of Metropolitan Roads, which put him in charge of all the roads in England. His road designs spread to the rest of Europe, and America's first macadam road was built in 1830. Eventually, new techniques improved the macadam design, like using asphalt to pave the top layer of the road. But we still call airport runways "tarmacs" in his honor.

McAdam's roads immediately improved life for millions of people—years before the automobile was ever invented. They allowed farmers to travel to markets, people to get to their jobs, and kids to get to school. McAdam made travel easier than it had been since the days of the Roman Empire.

Jonh Loudon McAdam

Cyrus McCormick

Some inventions are created to make a business more productive. "Productivity" is a measure of how much product a business can produce, compared with how much work it takes to produce it. When it's applied to farming, productivity determines how much crops a farmer can grow, divided by how much effort it took to grow them--and how much money they had to spend on planting and harvesting them. The more productive a farmer is, the more crops they can grow each year. And when Cyrus McCormick invented a mechanical reaper, it made farmers more productive than they ever had been before.

McCormick was born February 9, 1809 in Rockbridge County, Virginia. His father, Robert McCormick, was a farmer and a blacksmith. As a boy, Cyrus McCormick spent much time in his father's workshop, where he learned how to fix machines and invent new ones. Robert McCormick had invented many new machines to use on their farm, but he failed to invent a mechanical harvester. When Cyrus was twenty-two years old, he decided to give it a try.

Before Cyrus McCormick's time, harvesting was done without machines. When it was time for the fall harvest, a farmer and their farmhands would use sharp, curved metal tools called scythes to cut down all their crops by hand. This could take a long time: even an experienced farmer could only clear about two acres a day with a scythe. If their farm had hundreds of acres of crops, it could take weeks to harvest them all. Farmers needed a machine that could do the harvesting for them. But, so far, nobody had come up with one that worked.

McCormick introduced his first mechanical reaper in 1831. It was essentially a sled pulled by a team of horses. The sled held a wheel with an attached blade. When the wheel turned, it moved the blade in a back-and-forth sawing motion. As the horses pulled the sled through a field of crops, the McCormick Reaper swept up the crops and cut the seeds away from the stalks. It only required one farm worker, who would walk beside the sled and sweep up all the stalks with a rake. Using a McCormick Reaper, that one worker could now harvest about ten acres of crops a day, which made the process five times more productive than before.

McCormick received a patent for his reaper in 1834, but it wasn't immediately successful. His reaper was noisy, and it didn't work on some types of terrain. He spent the next several years perfecting his design, and they finally started to sell. In 1847, McCormick moved his family from Virginia to Chicago, Illinois and built a factory to produce McCormick Reapers. Although other inventors claimed they had already invented a mechanical reaper, McCormick was able to prove that his design was original. He sold more and more reapers and became rich. In 1851, he debuted his reaper at the Great Exhibition in London, where it did better than an English-built harvester. This event introduced the McCormick Reaper to the world.

The overall effect of the McCormick Reaper was to increase farmers' productivity. Now that farmers could clear land faster, they could plant more and more crops. This resulted in more food being available. Food prices fell and became more affordable for more people, and food shortages were less common. This improved living conditions for people around the world.

Richard Gatling

Richard Gatling was a lifelong inventor who was always looking for a new problem to solve. He invented many different things for many different industries, which improved the world and helped countless people. Although he devoted his life to making people's lives better, today he's mainly known for one invention that hurt people: the Gatling gun.

Gatling was born September 12, 1818, in Maneys Neck, North Carolina. His father, Jordan Gatling, built and improved machines used in farming, and his father's workshop was where he became familiar with machines and how they worked. Gatling began building inventions in 1839. He perfected the design for screw propellers on steamships, but another inventor had already come up with a similar one a few months earlier. His next inventions were more successful. He improved the design of a machine that could plant cotton to allow it to plant other crops like rice and wheat. He invented a machine that could more easily break up dense hemp fibers, and, in 1857, he invented a plow powered by steam. In his later years, he received a patent for a tractor, as well as for designs that improved bicycles and toilets. At one point in the 1850s, he even studied medicine and earned a medical degree, although he never worked as a doctor.

Guns have been used in war for about a thousand years. In Gatling's time, armies used cannons and individual soldiers used rifles or pistols. In the Union Army, a soldier had to reload their rifle each time they fired it, which meant that a soldier could only fire two or three times every minute. Additionally, rifles could easily get dirty or break and be unable to fire.

When the American Civil War began in 1861, Gatling began working on a new kind of gun that could fire faster and more reliably than a soldier's rifle. It helped that a new type of ammunition had just been invented. Previously, a soldier had to load gunpowder into their gun along with the bullet, but this new brass bullet already had gunpowder inside of it.

In 1862, Gatling debuted the first design of his Gatling gun. To operate it, a gunner would turn a hand crank that rotated and fired the barrels. The original Gatling gun had six .58 caliber barrels that could fire three hundred fifty bullets a minute. Later, Gatling updated it to ten .30 caliber barrels that could fire four hundred bullets a minute. Although Gatling was himself a Confederate sympathizer, he sold the Gatling gun to the Union Army, and it was first used in battle in 1864. It was the world's first machine gun.

The introduction of the Gatling gun was too late to affect the outcome of the Civil War. But the U.S. Army made it an official weapon in 1866, and used it for decades afterward until it was replaced by modern machine guns. The main benefit of the Gatling gun was that it could fire so many more bullets. This was an advantage if one army had a Gatling gun and the other didn't. The Gatling gun revolutionized warfare, but it also helped America, and many European countries, overpower indigenous peoples and take their lands.

Richard Gatling

John Wesley Hyatt

Today, it's difficult to imagine the world without plastic. It's used to make everything from water bottles to smartphones to airplane windows, along with all our favorite toys. Plastic is so important because it can be shaped and molded into practically any object, which means that its uses are practically endless. Plastic isn't perfect--it's also harmful to the environment--but without it, the world we live in wouldn't be possible. And our modern plastics all started with John Wesley Hyatt.

Hyatt was born November 28, 1837, in Starkey, New York. He started working as a printer at the age of sixteen, and later he became an inventor. In Hyatt's time, many different products were made from animals. The ivory found in elephant tusks was used to make billiard balls and piano keys. Turtle shells were used to make buttons and eyeglasses. Horns and antlers were used to make furniture. While these products were popular, they also had limitations. Manufacturers could only make as many piano keys or eyeglasses as nature could provide. Even worse, they were driving animal populations to extinction.

It's said that necessity is the mother of invention, and there's no greater necessity than a large amount of money. In 1863, a billiard ball company offered a ten thousand dollar reward for anyone who could design a billiard ball that didn't use ivory. Hyatt saw the ad and was inspired.

Along with his brother Isaiah, John Wesley Hyatt experimented with different chemical formulas that could produce a substance similar to ivory. This billiard ball substitute needed to be something that could be polished to a smooth spherical shape, and also strong enough to withstand a hard strike from a billiard cue. The Hyatt brothers first stumbled on a substance made of wood pulp and shellac. It wasn't strong enough to make a billiard ball, but it was a great material for making dominos and checker pieces, and the brothers started a side business selling them.

They continued their experiments, and in 1869, they finally discovered a substance that worked. By combining nitrocellulose, (a flammable material that's the main ingredient in gunpowder), camphor (the wax-like resin from the camphor tree), and alcohol, the brothers created a new material called celluloid. Celluloid was durable, and, just as important, it could be molded into almost any shape. The Hyatt brothers patented it in 1870, and they started a celluloid factory in 1872. But they never did receive that reward money.

Celluloid was first used as an ivory substitute, but manufacturers quickly realized it could be used for many more applications. It was used to make jewelry, combs, toothbrushes, dice, and playing cards. It was added to fabrics to make them stiffer. It was used to make film for still and movie cameras, which created the photography and movie and television industries. Eventually, celluloid was replaced with synthetic plastics, making it the ancestor of all the plastic we have today.

JOHN WESLEY HYATT

Ferdinand Von Zeppelin

If you've ever watched a live sporting event, you may have seen the Goodyear Blimp flying overhead. This is a descendant of the lighter-than-air hydrogen-powered airships of the early twentieth century. At one point, people thought airships would become the dominant form of air transportation. Airplanes and helicopters would eventually prove them wrong. But we still remember them today, along with their inventor, Ferdinand von Zeppelin.

Ferdinand von Zeppelin was born July 8, 1838, in Konstanz, a town in the Grand Duchy of Baden, which is in modern-day Germany. He was born into a wealthy Prussian family and educated by private tutors, and when he became an adult he joined the military. But he also studied different sciences, like chemistry and engineering, and this would prove to be an advantage later in his life.

In 1863, the Prussian government sent him to America to study techniques being used by the Union Army, and in St. Paul, Minnesota, he met Thaddeus S. C. Lowe. Lowe was an inventor and an expert in building hot-air balloons, which had recently been invented in France. Zeppelin was impressed with Lowe's hot-air balloons, and he saw many uses for both military and civilian applications. Zeppelin returned to his army career but never forgot about airships. In 1874, he made his first design for an airship with a rigid frame, which he called a zeppelin.

By 1890, Zeppelin left the army and began building his airship. His zeppelin design used a series of large metal rings. Inside the rings was a balloon that was filled with hydrogen--a gas lighter than air, and the reason why a zeppelin can float. It was controlled by a small compartment, located on the underside of the balloon, called a gondola. The rigid frame, Zeppelin believed, would allow him to build an airship that was even bigger than a hot-air balloon and could fly a much longer distance

In 1900, he completed his first zeppelin, the LZ-1, and took it on its first flight--three years before the Wright Brothers would make their first flight. At first, the LZ-1 could only travel a short distance, but Zeppelin kept perfecting it. By 1906, he had built over twenty zeppelins, and over thirty thousand people had flown in them. His zeppelin became so popular that other airships are still often called zeppelins even though they have different names.

Airplanes were being developed at the same time. But for the first several decades of the twentieth century, it looked like zeppelins would become the most popular form of air transportation because they were cheaper to make and maintain and could travel farther. Zeppelins were used throughout World War I for reconnaissance and bombing missions. In the 1930s, zeppelins were used for commercial flights.

But zeppelins could also be dangerous, especially since hydrogen gas is combustible. In 1937, millions of people were shocked by newsreel footage of the Hindenburg airship explosion. Meanwhile, engineers designed bigger airplanes that could fly farther and carry more passengers. Airships fell out of popularity, and they're rarely seen today. But the zeppelin still played an important role in aviation history.

Ferdinand Von Zeppelin

Wilhelm Conrad Röntgen

Light is one of the fundamental parts of our world. It's what allows us to see. But while humans have known about light for as long as we've been around, it's only recently that we've begun to understand it. In the nineteenth century, scientists discovered that the visible light we can see is only one type of light's varieties. Light exists on a spectrum, and different kinds of light operate on different wavelengths. These wavelengths can be thousands of miles long, or smaller than a nucleus. As scientists began to discover the different kinds of light, they also discovered different uses for them. One of these scientists was Wilhelm Conrad Röntgen.

Röntgen was born March 27, 1845, in Lennep, Prussia, in what's now Germany. He was the only child of a cloth manufacturer and merchant. As a boy, he wasn't a devoted student. But he enjoyed science, and he loved making machines. He studied mechanical engineering at the University of Utrecht, and he received his PhD in 1869.

Röntgen was a professor at different universities from then until 1920. He published papers on many different topics, such as the properties of gases, heat conductivity in crystals, and the electrical properties of quartz. But he made his greatest discovery in 1895.

That year, Röntgen was doing an experiment with a cathode ray tube, which is a glass tube that can produce a beam of electrons called a cathode ray. Nearby, Röntgen also had a paper plate coated in a substance called barium platinocyanide. Röntgen pointed the electron beam at the paper plate and was surprised to find that the paper plate had a fluorescent glow. Then Röntgen stuck his hand into the beam of electrons. It blocked the electrons, but Röntgen was surprised to discover that he could see the bones in his hand. Finally, he put a put a piece of photo film between his hand and the plate, and created the first X-ray image.

Röntgen knew that he had discovered a new type of radiation, which meant that he had found a new wavelength on the electromagnetic spectrum. He called this discovery X-radiation. This was later shortened to "X-ray." Before this, nobody knew that X-rays existed, much less how to see them.

The discovery of the X-ray itself was important. But soon, other scientists began finding new uses for it. The X-ray's most useful property was that it could pass through objects of some densities but not others. This effectively makes previously hidden objects visible, like the bones in Röntgen's hand.

For the first time, doctors could see inside a person's body without cutting them open. Within a year, doctors were using X-rays to make medical diagnoses. In England, Dr. John Hall-Edwards was one of the first doctors to use X-rays when he discovered a needle stuck in a patient's hand.

Soon, doctors also discovered that prolonged exposure to X-rays could be harmful to a person's health. Today, X-rays are used as little as possible, and patients and doctors have to be careful around them. But it's still a crucial tool for medical diagnoses, and it's saved countless lives. A unit of measurement that measures the amount of radiation in an X-ray was named the "roentgen" in Röntgen's honor.

Wilhelm Conrad Röntgen

Robert Hutchings Goddard

Very few inventions work the first time their inventor builds them. An invention typically takes many tries to develop and perfect before it's ready to be used. For some inventors, it can take years to prove their invention is useful. But once they do, their invention can make them wealthy and famous. Other inventors aren't so lucky. Their ideas and inventions are so ahead of their time that they might not be able to invent them in their lifetime, and it's only after their death that they get the credit they deserve. Robert Hutchings Goddard was one of the unluckier inventors. But, eventually, the world did recognize him for his ideas about rocket propulsion.

Goddard was born on October 5, 1882, in Worcester, Massachusetts. He lived in a time when scientific inventions were already changing the world. In the 1880s, electricity was brought to American cities, and the young Goddard was impressed. His parents encouraged him to study the world and to perform his own science experiments. It was the publication of H.G. Wells's *The War of the Worlds* in 1898 that first inspired Goddard's interest in traveling to outer space. A year later, he had a dream about building a working space rocket. He would spend the rest of his life trying to make this dream a reality.

Goddard enrolled in college in 1904, and as an undergraduate he was already coming up with ideas for new types of transportation, like a car that traveled through a system of vacuum tubes propelled by electromagnets. He also came up with his first idea for a liquid-fuel rocket. But he needed to make several more discoveries before he could build it.

He received his PhD from Clark University in 1911, and he spent the next several years researching the principles of propulsion. He proved that a rocket could be propelled in a vacuum like outer space, without needing the Earth's atmosphere to push against. He studied several kinds of liquid fuels to determine which one was best for a rocket. The challenge was finding a fuel that could provide enough energy to lift a rocket off the ground and break free from Earth's gravity. In 1914, he received patents for both a liquid-fuel rocket and a multi-stage solid-fuel rocket.

Goddard didn't just have to study how rockets could work; he also had to convince his fellow scientists that his ideas were possible--which didn't always go well. In 1920, he first suggested that a rocket might be able to fly to the moon, forty-nine years before humans actually did it. Other scientists mocked him, giving him the nickname "Moony Goddard."

But in 1926, Goddard finally proved that rocket flight was possible. At his Aunt Effie's farm in Auburn, Massachusetts, he completed his first successful liquid-fuel rocket launch. It didn't get very high off the ground, but it proved that his theories could work.

Goddard spent the 1930s and 40s perfecting his rocket designs and helping design weapons for the U.S. Military in World War II. He died in 1945, just before the beginning of the Space Age. After his death, his wife Esther publicized his career so he wouldn't be forgotten. In 1960, the U.S. Government paid her a one million dollar settlement for using her husband's patents. And in 1961, NASA named the Goddard Space Flight Center in his honor. Today, he's remembered as the father of American rocketry.

Clarence Birdseye

Not all inventions need to completely change the world. Sometimes, it's enough to just make life easier. The invention of frozen foods made it possible to keep and store food for up to months at a time. Even fully cooked foods can be frozen and thawed in a fraction of the time it would have taken to prepare them at home. All of us have eaten frozen foods, and we all owe Clarence Birdseye a thank-you for making our lives better.

Clarence Birdseye was born on December 9, 1886 in Brooklyn, New York. He was always interested in science, especially natural sciences. He loved collecting insects so much that his classmates nicknamed him "Bugs." He went to college but had to drop out after two years because he couldn't afford tuition. Instead, he went to work for the U.S. Department of Agriculture. He spent his first years working as a taxidermist and a naturalist controlling coyote populations. In 1910 and 1911, he worked with disease expert Willard von Orstel King to collect hundreds of small mammals and study the ticks on them. Because of this, von Orstel King was able to prove that ticks were the cause of Rocky Mountain spotted fever.

In 1912, Birdseye moved to Labrador, Newfoundland, Canada to work as a fur trapper, and this was when he made his biggest discovery. Before Birdseye, people did freeze their food, but the freezing process ruined the flavor. In Labrador, a group of Inuits taught Birdseye how to ice fish. Birdseye noticed that the fish he caught froze almost immediately when exposed to the cold air (below -40°C), but when it was thawed it still tasted good, even months later. Birdseye realized that the secret to freezing foods was doing it quickly.

He returned to the United States, and in 1924, he helped found the General Seafoods Company to sell flash-frozen fish. Since the climate was much warmer than Labrador, he had to invent a process that could freeze food quickly. To do this, he would place packaged frozen food between two hollow metal plates that were chilled by evaporating ammonia. He sold frozen fish for a few years. Then, in 1927, he expanded his operations to include meat, poultry, fruit, and vegetables.

His business made him rich, but frozen foods didn't immediately become popular. It wasn't until World War II, when food shortages led to a lack of canned goods, that Americans started eating frozen foods regularly. Once Americans realized how much more convenient they were, frozen foods were here to stay. In the 1950s, frozen TV dinners became one of the country's most popular meals.

Frozen foods were just one of Clarence Birdseye's inventions. He held over three hundred patents for inventions like an infrared heat lamp, a harpoon gun without recoil, and a system for dehydrating food. But none of these were as influential as his frozen foods system. Today, the Bird's Eye line of frozen foods is still sold worldwide.

Igor Sikorsky

When it comes to the history of flight, most people think of the Wright brothers and airplanes. But the history of flight also includes helicopters, which, unlike airplanes, can make "vertical flights." Most helicopters can't fly as high or as far as most airplanes, but they offer many advantages airplanes don't: They don't require much room to take off or land, and, most importantly, they can hover. So, when we talk about the history of flight, we should also include Igor Sikorsky, the man who invented the helicopter.

Sikorsky was born on May 25, 1889 in Kiev, in what was then the Russian Empire but is now the Ukraine. Sikorsky was interested in the possibility of building a helicopter at a young age. His mother Mariya loved art and introduced him to the work of Renaissance artist Leonardo da Vinci. As we saw in the da Vinci section, Leonardo came up with a design for a helicopter using a rotating screw in the fifteenth century, but since motors didn't exist, it was impossible to build. Centuries later, these drawings inspired the young Sikorsky to one day try to make them real. He started early. When he was just twelve years old, he made a toy rubber band helicopter that could actually take off.

Sikorsky studied engineering in Paris and St. Petersburg, and in 1908 and 1909, he tried to build his first helicopter. It couldn't fly. Just like da Vinci, Sikorski didn't have a powerful enough engine to build a helicopter. Disappointed, he decided to design airplanes instead.

In 1913, Sikorsky designed and built the world's first four-engine airplane, called the Sikorsky Russky Vityaz, or the Russian Knight. A year later, he debuted an even more powerful version that he named the Ilya Muromets, after a Russian folk hero. Sikorsky originally planned for his aircraft to be used for transporting passengers, but when World War I broke out, the Russian military converted it to a bomber. He received the Cross of St. Vladimir for his efforts.

In the chaos brought by the end of World War I and the Russian Revolution, Sikorsky decided to move to America to start an airplane company. His company designed several successful airplanes in the 1920s and 30s. But by the end of the decade, engine technology had advanced enough for Sikorsky to finally build his helicopter.

In 1939, Sikorsky and his company designed and built the VS-300, and on September 14, Sikorsky made the first successful test flight. Just like he had back in 1913, Sikorsky personally piloted the VS-300 on its maiden voyage, believing that the aircraft's designer should always be the first person to test it out. It was the world's first helicopter flight. By 1941, he had improved his design enough to fly for an hour and thirty-two minutes.

Sikorsky imagined the VS-300 could be used for peaceful purposes, especially rescuing people trapped in natural disasters like floods or avalanches. Just like what happened with the Russian Knight years earlier, however, his helicopter was eventually used for warfare. Even so, by the end of his life, Sikorsky was proud to know his helicopters had already saved over fifty thousand people's lives.

Ernest Lawrence

In the early twentieth century, the discovery of subatomic particles completely changed the world. Not only did this discovery prove that there was something even smaller than the atom, it also suggested that subatomic particles could be used for many different purposes. It's one thing to discover that subatomic particles exist. It's another thing entirely to figure out how to manipulate them and unlock the huge amounts of energy they contain. Before subatomic particles could be studied, there first had to be a device that could study them. This device is called a particle accelerator, or a cyclotron, and it was invented by Ernest Lawrence.

Ernest Lawrence, the grandson of Norwegian immigrants, was born August 8 1901 in Canton, South Dakota. Radio technology was brand-new, and as a boy Ernest enjoyed tinkering with electronic radio transmitters. He originally planned to become a doctor. A mentor, however, convinced him to switch to physics. He proved to be a brilliant student, and in 1925, he received his PhD from Yale.

Lawrence went to work as a professor at the University of California Berkeley. At this time, the science of particle physics was practically brand-new. Scientists were just beginning to understand that if a subatomic particle could be propelled at a high enough speed, and then smashed into an atom, it could produce huge amounts of energy, or even create brand-new elements. In 1929, Lawrence read an article in a physics journal that explained how to build a particle accelerator. Lawrence knew it was too big and expensive to build at Berkeley, so he designed a smaller and cheaper one. Lawrence completed his first cyclotron in 1932. It was twenty-seven inches in diameter, and it used an eighty-ton magnet.

For about the next decade, Lawrence and his team focused on perfecting their cyclometer while other scientists made important discoveries about subatomic particles. But Lawrence and his team still made many discoveries of their own. They were the first scientists to synthesize technetium, a periodic table element that doesn't appear in nature. They also discovered that radioactive phosphorus isotopes could be used to create gamma rays, which can be used to treat some types of cancer. In 1939, Lawrence received the Nobel Prize for his discoveries.

During World War II, Lawrence joined the Manhattan Project, the top-secret program to build the first nuclear bomb. For this, Lawrence invented another machine called a calutron, which used electromagnets to separate the uranium-235 isotopes used to power the bomb. In other words, his machine created the fuel that made the nuclear bomb possible.

Like some of the other inventions in this collection, Lawrence's cyclotron had both harmful and helpful uses. It led to the development of nuclear weapons, but it also created medical technology that's saved millions of lives. Lawrence's discovery helped to usher in a new scientific age. Shortly after his death, both the Lawrence Berkeley National Laboratory and the Lawrence Livermore National Laboratory were named after him. Three years later, a new element added to the periodic table was named "Lawrencium" in his honor.

Alan Turing

Today's computers can do so many things. Take the average smartphone. With the apps on a smartphone, a user can make a phone call, they can find themselves on a map, they can plan a fitness regimen, and they can even take a picture of their cat and share it online. Computers can do so many things that it can be difficult to understand exactly what a computer is. The simplest definition of a computer is that it's a machine that can be programmed to perform math equations. Since computers can do math equations much faster than a human brain, this allows computers to perform complicated functions, like keeping an airplane in the air. The modern ancestor of the computer in your pocket dates back to the 1930s, and a British scientist named Alan Turing.

Alan Turing was born June 23, 1912, in London, England. His father was a civil servant who was often stationed in India during Turing's childhood. From a young age, he was interested in math and science, especially new scientific fields like quantum physics and the theory of relativity, and even when he was a child he understood these subjects at an adult level. He graduated from the University of Cambridge in 1934.

Turing spent the first few years of his professional life studying computer theory. The British inventor Charles Babbage had already invented a calculating machine about a century earlier. But the twentieth century brought renewed interest in computers, and mathematicians like Turing first had to study how they worked in order to understand what they were capable of. In 1936, he came up with a theoretical invention he called a Turing Machine. With this, he mathematically proved that, instead of having to invent a different machine for every possible task, computer scientists could invent one machine that could do all tasks. The Turing Machine paved the way for the invention of today's computers.

During World War II, Turing lent his computational genius to the war effort. Nazi Germany was using an encoding device called an Enigma machine. An encoding device works by translating a written message into a secret code by scrambling the letters. The Enigma machine could create a secret code that was thought to be impossible to break without having a key. Turing's job was to take the Enigma machine apart to learn how it worked, and then invent a new machine that could crack the Enigma code. His "Bomba" machine successfully decoded German messages, and it helped England win the war. General Dwight Eisenhower estimated Turing's work shortened the war by two years and saved millions of lives.

After the war, Turing used his codebreaking experience to begin designing an electronic, programmable computer. It was called the Automatic Computing Engine, or ACE. The ACE was the world's first computer that could store and run computer programs. The first version was built in 1950. It would influence later machines like the Benix G-15, which is considered the first personal computer.

ALAN TURING

Frank Whittle

When the Wright brothers invented the airplane in 1903, it changed the way humans traveled. Airplanes meant that humans could cross greater distances in shorter amounts of time. Twenty-four years after the Wright brothers, Charles Lindbergh completed the first solo flight across the Atlantic Ocean in just thirty-four hours, a journey that would have taken several days by ship. But as impressive as early airplanes were, they can't compete with today's jetliners. A modern commercial jet can fly from New York City to London, England in five to six hours. How did today's planes become so much more powerful? Because of a British aviation engineer named Frank Whittle.

Whittle was born June 1, 1907 in Coventry, England, the son of a factory foreman. Airplanes had just been invented a few years earlier, and the young Whittle was captivated by flight. In 1923, Whittle turned eighteen and tried to join the recently created Royal Air Force as a pilot. But he was rejected for being too short. He applied two more times and was finally admitted as an apprentice mechanic. In 1928, he became a fighter pilot, and he later studied at the RAF engineering school.

While Whittle was training to be a pilot, he began to think about ways to make airplanes fly longer distances. At the time, airplanes used propellers or piston engines, which could only enable a plane to fly so high. At these low altitudes, wind resistance slowed planes down. Whittle believed the solution was to make planes fly at even higher altitudes, where there was less wind resistance. To do this, he needed to invent an even more powerful engine. He theorized that it would either need to be powered either by rocket propulsion or a gas turbine.

In 1930, he received a patent for his first turbojet engine, which used a gas turbine. Unlike a piston engine, his turbojet engine injected a constant stream of fuel into its combustion chamber. An air compressor on the front of the engine pushed air into the combustion chamber, where it met the flame. This would blast hot air through a turbine, which creates the backwards force needed to propel the plane forward.

At first, the RAF didn't see the need for his jet engine, so he went into business himself. In 1936, he started a company called Power Jets Ltd, and a year later he tested his first jet engine on the ground.

But Whittle was just one inventor working on a more powerful aircraft engine. In 1939, the German physicist Hans Pabst von Ohain flew the first successful flight with a jet engine. In response, the RAF accelerated Whittle's project. Whittle built his own jet aircraft and flew its first successful test flight in 1941. Whittle's aircraft were so fast they could be used to intercept German V-1 rockets, and they helped Britain win the war.

After the war, British companies began developing jet engines for commercial air travel. In 1952, the world's first commercial jet airliner, the Havilland DH 106, made its first flight. Piston engines could only travel at a maximum speed of 180 miles per hour, but the Havilland could top out at 450 miles per hour. The commercial aviation industry took off, and people have been traveling faster and farther than ever before.

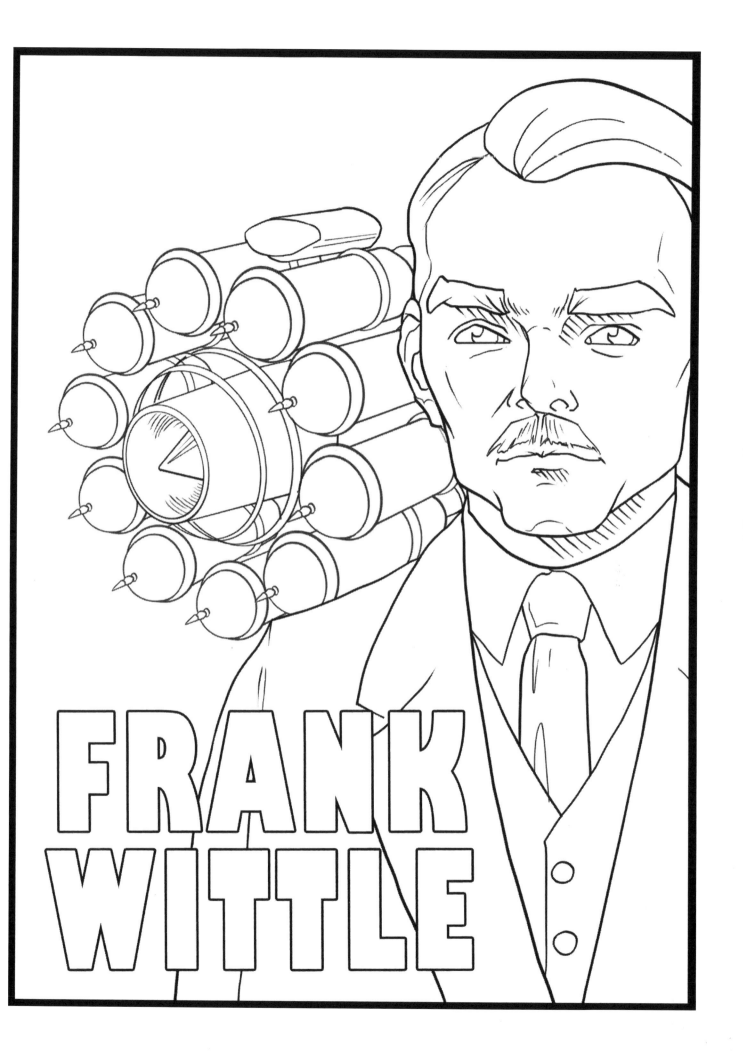

FRANK
WITTLE

Edward Teller

The invention of nuclear weapons is one of the defining moments of the twentieth century, and one of the most controversial. Nuclear weapons have only been used in warfare twice, when the United States dropped atomic bombs on the Japanese cities of Hiroshima and Nagasaki in 1945. Today's nuclear weapons are many times more powerful, and the radioactive fallout they create is capable of ending life on Earth. Edward Teller is the man responsible for making the most powerful nuclear weapons, and he believed they could be used to stop wars from starting in the first place.

Teller was born January 15, 1908, in Budapest, Hungary. His birth occurred just eleven years after J.J. Thompson discovered the electron. When Teller was born, scientists were just beginning to understand atoms and subatomic particles, how they worked, and what they could be used for. During the early part of his career, Teller was one of the scientists who studied subatomic particles and described their characteristics. He studied chemical engineering and physical chemistry and earned a PhD in 1930. In his doctoral thesis, he described how electrons in hydrogen molecules behave. He moved to the United States in 1935, and he classified all the ways subatomic particles exit a nucleus during atomic decay.

When World War II began in 1939, President Franklin Delano Roosevelt called for America's scientists to use their knowledge to defend the country, and Teller was inspired to devote the rest of his career to the development of nuclear weapons. In 1941, he was part of Enrico Fermi's team at the University of Chicago that produced the first nuclear chain reaction, an important step on the way to making the atomic bomb. In 1943, he joined the secret lab at Los Alamos to build the first atomic bomb.

The Los Alamos laboratory was working to build an atomic bomb that explodes via a fission reaction, which is caused by splitting the atom of a uranium-235 isotope. While working at Los Alamos, Teller realized it was possible to build an even bigger bomb that used a fusion reaction. This was called a hydrogen bomb. Essentially, a hydrogen bomb works by first splitting a fission core and causing a nuclear detonation. Then, it uses the energy from that explosion to compress a second core and create an even bigger explosion. But the Los Alamos laboratory continued with its original atomic bomb plan, and it helped end the war in 1945.

By 1949, the Soviet Union developed their own atomic bomb, putting them on equal footing with America. Teller knew that his hydrogen bomb could once again give America a nuclear advantage. This convinced President Harry Truman to sponsor his H-bomb project. Teller successfully tested his H-bomb at the Enewetak Atoll on November 1, 1952. The explosion was equivalent to ten million tons of TNT.

The H-Bomb ensured that the Cold War and nuclear arms race between America and the Soviet Union would continue for several more decades. But neither side ever used the nuclear weapons they built.

Michael DeBakey

As we've seen with many of the other inventors in this collection, sometimes an invention is only possible after another invention is made first. In the nineteenth and early twentieth centuries, scientists made big discoveries in many different fields including electricity, mechanical engineering, plastics, X-rays, sanitation, and more. Future generations of scientists and inventors were then able to use these discoveries to make new inventions. In the middle of the twentieth century, Dr. Michael DeBakey relied on decades of previous innovation to invent many new medical devices and techniques that have saved millions of lives.

Michael DeBakey was born September 7, 1908, in Lake Charles, Louisiana. He was the son of Lebanese immigrants, and his father worked as a pharmacist. As a boy, DeBakey helped his father in his pharmacy. As a result, he decided to pursue a career in medicine. He enrolled in Tulane University and received his medical degree in 1932.

To understand DeBakey's accomplishments, it helps to first understand the human circulatory system. We breathe in through our lungs, and our lungs pass the oxygen from our breath into our bloodstream. Then, the heart acts as a pump to circulate oxygenated blood to the rest of our body. The heart is one of the body's most important organs, and people can only survive for a few minutes if it stops pumping. This means if something is ever wrong with a person's heart--like heart disease, or a defect--it's extremely difficult to fix it. In order to fix a heart, a surgeon first needs to stop the heart, which is very dangerous to the patient's health. In the early twentieth century, surgeons had developed techniques to pause the heart for about fifteen minutes at a time, which wasn't enough time to fix many of the heart's worst problems. They needed a way to stop the heart longer and still keep their patient alive. Many surgeons thought this would never be possible.

In 1932, DeBakey invented a device called a "roller pump." It was a type of pump connected to rubber tubing, and a surgeon could use a roller pump to circulate a patient's blood. Essentially, a roller pump acted like a second heart while the surgeon operated on the patient. After DeBakey invented it, Drs. John Gibbon and J.Y. Templeton used it to perfect their own invention, called a heart-lung machine. Their heart machine allowed surgeons to operate on hearts for up to an hour. On May 6, 1953, Dr. Gibbon performed the world's first successful open-heart surgery using a heart-lung machine.

Dr. DeBakey made several other medical innovations during his career. In 1953, he invented a technique to replace damaged blood vessels with plastic tubing. Also In 1953, he performed the first surgery to successfully remove plaque from a carotid artery. In 1964, he performed the first successful coronary artery bypass surgery. And in 1966, he was the first surgeon to successfully implant a device that helped a patient's heart beat. Today he's remembered most for his contributions to the heart-lung machine. Just as Dr. DeBakey helped to improve open-heart surgery techniques during his career, today's doctors have found ways to improve Dr. DeBakey's techniques, like replacing the roller pump with a centrifugal pump. But every year, about nine hundred thousand people receive open-heart surgery using techniques pioneered by Dr. DeBakey. His work has saved millions of lives.

Douglas Engelbart

As we saw with the stories of Charles Babbage and Alan Turing, computers took over one hundred years to develop, starting out as mechanical counting devices and progressing to machines that could perform complicated questions in seconds. In the middle of the twentieth century, computers were changing the way math and science were done. But they still required many years of training and specialization for a scientist to use them. To get to the personal computers of the 1980s and 90s, and then to the smartphones we all have in our pockets, computers needed to get a lot easier to use. And Douglas Engelbart made computers easier for everyone.

Engelbart was born on January 30, 1925, in Portland, Oregon. He showed an early aptitude for technology. During World War II, he worked as a radar technician for the U.S. Navy. After the war, he studied electrical engineering.

At this time, computers were almost brand-new. To operate them, a user had to input a series of paper punch cards--similar to the ones Joseph-Marie Jacquard used to program his automatic loom--into the computer. The computer would then perform its calculations and print them out. This process could take many hours to complete and errors were common. If the user made a mistake at any point in the process, all their work would be wasted.

Engelbart didn't find his electrical engineering work challenging. He wanted to use his science abilities to make the world a better place. In 1950, he had an idea that he would spend the rest of his life working on. As a radar technician, he remembered using radar consoles with screens that displayed all the necessary information he needed. He called it a "graphical user interface," and it led to the screens we use on our smartphones and laptops today.

In 1956, he went to work at the Stanford Research Institute, and for the next decade, he developed many of his ideas for the graphical interface. These included computer screens that used bitmap displays; the ability to display multiple computer programs or windows at the same time on the same computer screen; and the ability to hyperlink, or link to multiple kinds of media like videos, photos, or sounds within the same document. Some time before 1965, he and another engineer named Bill English invented the computer mouse. For decades, the mouse was the most common device people used to interact with their computers before it was mostly replaced by today's touchscreens and touchpads.

In 1968, he held a conference and invited the world's top computer scientists to see his inventions. He used his newly invented mouse, and a computer keyboard, to demonstrate techniques like text editing, hyperlinking, and using multiple windows. He was even able to demonstrate the world's first video conference via a computer. Not only did this demonstration show computer scientists an easier way to use computers, it led to the personal computer revolution. In the 1980s, people like Apple founder Steve Jobs used Engelbart's inventions to build and sell the first computers everyone could use. Engelbart's inventions didn't make him rich, but he definitely made the world a better place like he had set out to do.

Marie Curie

The discoveries of radiation and radioactive elements were some of the most important discoveries of the twentieth centuries, because they led to fundamental improvements in medicine and nuclear power. Marie Curie's contributions to our understanding of radiation would be enough for her to be remembered forever. But she was also a pioneer who paved the way for the generations of female scientists who came after her.

Marie Curie was born Maria Skłodowska, on November 7, 1867 in Warsaw, Poland. She was extremely smart as a child and had a strong memory, and when she was sixteen she won a gold medal for her scholastic achievements. She moved to Paris in 1891 to study at the Sorbonne, one of Europe's most important schools. She received degrees in physical sciences in 1893 and mathematics in 1894. She also met her future husband, fellow scientist Pierre Curie. They married in 1895 and began working together.

In 1896, another scientist named Henri Becquerel made a discovery that influenced Marie's research: radiation. Radiation is a natural phenomenon that occurs in certain elements on the periodic table. The atoms in these elements can be unstable, which means their nucleuses can spontaneously break apart. When this happens, the nucleus gives off energy called radiation. These elements are called "radioactive." Radiation is important because it can be used for many different purposes, like treating cancers. But too much exposure to radiation can also be harmful to humans.

Becquerel discovered radiation in the element uranium. Marie wanted to see if radiation could be found in other elements. She discovered thorium at the same time as another scientist, G.C. Schmidt. Then she began to study a mineral called pitchblade, which is often found with uranium deposits. This led Marie to discover a new element on the periodic table, which she named polonium in honor of her homeland of Poland. Shortly after, her study of pitchblade led to the discovery of another new element called radium. In 1903, she, Pierre, and Henri Becquerel shared the Nobel Prize for Physics. Marie was the first woman to ever win the award.

Pierre died in 1906, but Marie continued their work. That year, she filled Pierre's position at the Sorbonne and became the university's first female professor. Marie understood that radioactive elements were important and needed to be studied further. The problem was, these elements were difficult to obtain--many tons of pitchblade needed to be mined in order to produce a tiny amount of polonium and radium. In 1911, Marie received the Nobel Prize for Chemistry for isolating pure radium. She's still the only woman who has ever won the award in two different categories.

Marie spent the rest of her life studying radiation and giving speeches urging the world to do the same. She convinced many governments to spend resources gathering more radioactive material for study, and this led to many more important breakthroughs, like the discovery of the neutron in 1934. That same year, Marie died of cancer due to her many years of exposure to radioactive materials. She gave her life for the advancement of science, and she's still an inspiration today.

Josephine Cochrane

Anyone who's ever washed dishes by hand knows how much of a convenience a dishwasher is. Washing dishes by hand means having to scrub food off each dish and cup, and particularly tough food stains can require real effort. Cleaning up after a meal for a large family can take hours, but a dishwasher eliminates a lot of that work. Even better, a dishwasher's jets of very hot water mean that dishes can be sanitized more so than by hand. By inventing the dishwasher, Josephine Cochrane saved millions of people countless hours of effort, and she's made our dishes cleaner than they were before.

She was born Josephine Garis in Ashtabula County, Ohio, on March 8, 1839. Her great-grandfather was an inventor who developed steamboat inventions. In 1848, she married William Cochran and took his name, but she preferred to spell it with an "e" on the end. Her husband opened a dry goods store and became wealthy, and Cochrane enjoyed the life of a homemaker and socialite. In 1870, the Cochranes moved to Chicago, where they enjoyed entertaining guests at their mansion. One morning after a dinner party, Cochrane discovered that her servants had carelessly chipped her fine china while washing it. She decided to find a better way to wash dishes.

In the 1850s and 60s, other inventors had tried to invent a machine that could wash dishes. One was a hand-cranked dishwasher, and another was a dishwasher that rotated plates through a tub of water. But these didn't work. Cochrane first designed wire compartments that could hold dishes, cups, and saucers--similar to the wire racks in dishwashers today. These containers went inside a copper boiler. Inside the boiler and below the racks, a motor-powered wheel would spin and spray soapy hot water on the dishes. The first several men she hired to build her dishwasher tried to improve on her design, but none of these worked. Eventually, she found a mechanic named George Butters, and together they built her first dishwasher without changing her design. She received a patent in 1886, and then she founded the Garis-Cochrane Manufacturing Company, which was later renamed to the Cochran's Crescent Washing Machine Company.

Cochrane's machine was a hit with her friends, but her next goal was to market it to customers, which she did by advertising Cochrane Dishwashers in newspapers. Hotels and restaurants were immediately interested, but dishwashers weren't immediately popular for home buyers because most homes at the time didn't have access to enough hot water. She displayed her dishwasher at the 1893 Chicago World's Fair and won awards for both the design and its durability.

By the 1950s, advances in plumbing technology meant more American households had hot water, and dishwashers could be sold to many homes. Cochrane's Crescent Dishwashing Company eventually became KitchenAid, which is still one of the top dishwasher brands on the market today. Since Cochrane died in 1913, she didn't get to see her invention become as popular as it is today. In 2006, she was inducted into the Inventors' Hall of Fame.

THANK YOU!

Have questions? We want to hear from you!
Email us at: support@activitywizo.com

Please consider writing a review!
Just visit: activitywizo.com/review

Printed in Great Britain
by Amazon